The Daily T[elegraph]

THE BEST OF

1992

'When the German jumps,
we all jump'

CHAPMANS

Chapmans Publishers Ltd
141–143 Drury Lane
London WC2B 5TB

First published by Chapmans 1992

A CIP catalogue record for this book is available
from the British Library

ISBN 1 85592 635 0

Photoset in Linotron Times and Optima by
MC Typeset Ltd, Wouldham, Rochester, Kent
Printed and bound in Great Britain by
Clays Ltd, St Ives plc

THE BEST OF

1992

MATTHEW PRITCHETT was voted Granada's *What the Papers Say* Cartoonist of the Year in 1992. He studied at St Martin's School of Art in London and first saw himself published in the *New Statesman* during one of its rare lapses from high seriousness. He has been *The Daily Telegraph*'s front-page pocket cartoonist since 1988.

All the best,
Gene,
Albert & Anne

THE BEST OF

1992

*'It's very realistic – nobody
in it ever watches Eldorado'*

Home Affairs
Jani Allen lost her libel case against
Channel 4

'His champagne glass
is going up and down'

'There's that nice couple we
saw in the storm of '87'

Home Affairs

A huge motorway bridge got stuck while being moved

'If you must know, I was run over by a bridge'

'Maybe the person who valued my house would like to buy it'

Home Affairs
There was a new head of MI5, and a small
turn out in the local elections

*'You really are a master of
disguise, Mrs Rimington'*

*'Could I have another
recount?'*

Home Affairs

Scientists succeeded in creating nuclear
fusion – for a moment

*'Let's use the toaster for
now and we'll try nuclear
fusion again tomorrow'*

'Unplaced at Crufts again?'

Danger – Ravers at Work
New Age Travellers were a summer menace

*'You're going to meet a
tall dark stranger who
will arrest you'*

Singing in the Rain
Luciano Pavarotti gave a concert in
Hyde Park

'I've always wanted a
box at the opera'

Not Guilty, M'Lud
A defendant committed 274 offences while on bail

'And hurry up, I'm due back in court soon'

'Oh brilliant. I'm released just as the whole prison service is about to be reformed'

Not Guilty, M'Lud
Joyriding – an unwelcome cult

'I want you to get up to about 100 mph, pull on the handbrake, spin the vehicle and hit the horn'

'On second thoughts, could I have my brick back?'

No Room in the Ark
The closure of London Zoo was mooted

'Hello, it's about the bedsit
you advertised in the paper'

'For goodness sake
look cuddly'

'Do you remember
sponsoring me in 1987?'

The White House

President Bush was taken ill in Japan – could he still win?

'It's the moment all parents dread – when their child asks about the American electoral system'

'People don't usually pass out in Japanese restaurants until they see the bill'

'*I'd like to buy a ticket,
but not all at once*'

Trade Wars
Euro privateers pinched our fish but
turned down our lamb

*'I'm against closer links
with Europe, particularly
France'*

Alles Out
Germany went on strike for the first time in living memory

'I think it means "rubbish beginning to stink"'

'A rail strike? In Germany?'

The Election – Spending Plans

'I don't know how I'll
vote – I leave all that
to my accountant'

'I may be overdrawn, but
I'm expecting an electoral
bribe very shortly'

'If Labour gets in we could
cancel out our losses by
having 25 children'

'She says her husband earns
over £30,000, but she doesn't
look very worried'

The Election – Poll Wars

'Do you remember inter-viewing me for an opinion poll? Can I change my answers again?'

'I must warn you, he's extremely volatile'

'You're not going to put
me down as a margin of
error, are you?'

The Election – Party Politics

'And this shows how much air time will be taken up with meaningless charts'

'Brilliant! I'm alive for 10 hours and there's a drought and a general election'

'Party political broadcast on the NHS – Take Nine'

'We put them up when there's a row on TV about the NHS'

The Election – Personal Security
The Prime Minister was hit by an egg during the campaign

'No, it's not to throw at John Major'

'These are Mr Major's news-papers – I'm cutting out all the bits that might upset him'

Sporting Times

A British superbike struck gold at the Olympics

'It's a combination of the new superbike and the Spanish tummy bug'

Sporting Times

A drugs scandal marred the Olympics for Britain

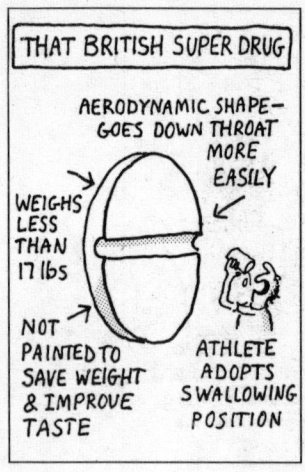

THAT BRITISH SUPER DRUG

AERODYNAMIC SHAPE—GOES DOWN THROAT MORE EASILY

WEIGHS LESS THAN 17 lbs

NOT PAINTED TO SAVE WEIGHT & IMPROVE TASTE

ATHLETE ADOPTS SWALLOWING POSITION

'Psst, there's someone at the finishing line who's interested in buying your house'

'*Could you slow down occasionally so people get a chance to read our logos?*'

'*I bought these South African oranges because I felt so guilty about the cricket*'

Sporting Times

Australia lost in the World Cup
rugby series

'Half mast'

Sporting Times

There was a fire at the Wolves ground

'It was a team effort. I'm over the moon for the lads'

Sporting Times
Paul Gascoigne went to Italy

*'I haven't got the heart to tell
them this isn't the
Wimbledon queue'*

Sporting Times

Jeremy Bates did well at Wimbledon

'*Do you have to grunt when you switch on the TV set?*'

'*I've never had to treat 1,200 people for shock before*'

The Citizen's Charter

'No room? What about the Citizen's Charter?'

'Your operation would have been on time but the surgeon's train was cancelled'

'Under the Citizen's Charter
they have to keep us better
informed'

'I was given it because my
train was 27 minutes late'

The Royal Year

Prince Charles criticized Common Market
cheese plans; the Yorks parted

'Whatever Prince Charles
says, I still don't
trust French cheese'

'My wife's left me. She
says I'm never at home'

'Is it true that Texans keep sensitive photos under their hats?'

'We've taken out an injunction to stop you showing us your holiday photos'

The Royal Year

'I want some financial advice but I'd rather keep my shoes on'

TV Wars

There were winners and losers when the new TV franchises were announced

'How much do I have to bid
to get this programme
taken off now?'

'And now, the test card and
some light music until 1993'

The Budget

'So you still believe in giveaway Budgets?'

The Budget

'Lend me a fiver, Jenkins'

'Oh no, I've run over the Tory candidate in my brand new cheaper car'

Political Affairs
The SDP – and then there were two

'And the result of the SDP leadership contest is: Rosie Barnes one vote, John Cartwright one vote'

'You deserve it'

'Why on earth did you ask
Mr Ashdown if he had
anything to declare?'

'Well where's Mr Mellor
with his eight records?

A Gale of a Time
The drought hit Britain's rivers

'And this is called the
Hosepipe Ban Garden'

'Have you ever wondered
why we have webbed feet?'

A Gale of a Time
Despite the drought, there were severe storms

'Don't worry, the lightning only hit our hosepipe'

At the Earth Summit in Rio

'Do you think the biodiversity
treaty could have saved
Gerald Kaufman?'

'Do you know, in a single
week an area the size of
Denmark pulls back
from the EC?'

'Oh yes, Mr Major, my people have lived here for a not inconsiderable period of time'

'Don't think of it as refusing to sign a treaty, think of it as conserving ink'

Home at Last

'There was some postage to pay on your postcard to Terry Waite'

'I think we should leave it a few days before we explain about this'

'Freed hostage? Take a seat
and we'll deal with you
as soon as possible'

'Mr Mann . . . Jackie, if there
were an election tomorrow,
who would you vote for?'

That Slump

'I'm interested in
obtaining one of these
imprudent loans'

Dear Mr Jenkins,
Profits have fallen by more
than £300m. We have charged
you £10 for this letter

'Look, this clearly shows an
economic upturn in the
second half of this year'

'That was the day I popped
out and bought a sandwich'

That Slump

'But, I think of my overdraft as a worldwide problem'

'Well, I don't call that a consumer led recovery'

*I'm afraid I'm going to have
to ask you to leave'*

*'This is the time for
short-term panic measures'*

That Slump

'*Happy New Year – but don't quote me on that*'

'*. . . And that brings to an end this meeting of the CBI*'

'Our departmental spending
allocation has just rolled
under the desk'

'Just get up there, stand
on the edge and think of
the economy'

That Slump

'Don't you feel on a day like this you just want to be out of the office?'

'I must say it's nice to see more women in senior positions in business'

'It's a marvel of evolution –
an out-of-worker bee'

'Tell me, why do they
call you Canary Wharf?'

That Slump

'*I think his business
confidence is picking up*'

'*They're waiting for the
price to drop by another
couple of thousand*'

That Slump

'Typical, they've reserved
the best spot on the ledge'

School's Out

The new education reforms began to be implemented

'We're the three wise men'

'We've had an attractive transfer offer for you from a school lower down the league'

'It's the trainee teachers that cause all this class-room overcrowding'

'I'm so worried by the new tests I can't concentrate on being a tree swaying in the wind'

School's Out

*'Good news — I've
bottomed out'*

*'I'm being kept informed
about the grave situation
concerning my GCSE results
but I don't see any need to
cut short my holiday'*

School's Out

Primary school teachers were told to stick to tried and test methods

'It's a picture of me rejecting the mindless iconoclasm of recent decades'

'I love my progressive primary school so I'm sending the Education Secretary an indignant collage'

Lean, Lean Fighting Machine

Defence cuts continued to trouble the
armed forces

*'A lot of the pageantry has
gone since the defence cuts'*

*'. . . and what's going to
happen to our regimental
mascot?'*

'*About this social chapter we've opted out of . . .*'

'*Don't follow that – it only leads to Maastricht*'

Europe – the Saga Continues

*'It's one of our concessions
over the Dutch treaty'*

*'I put the GB sticker on to
make it look more expensive'*

Maastricht – the Danes Say No

'And all those in favour of pillaging . . .'

'I think you've gone overboard on this referendum business'

Maastricht – Final Indecision

'*Oh shut up about having a say*'

'*In this version he can't decide whether to ratify the Maastricht treaty*'

Church Times

A plea for contraception, and a bolting
Irish bishop

'Anything for the world
population crisis, sir?'

'Just a minute – you mean
people get offered £100,000
to keep quiet?'

Church Times

'The vicar's trying to compete with the Sunday-opening supermarkets'

'I've warned you, bishop . . . no politics'

'Is this British Telecom head office?'

'Are you being fattened up for privatisation, grandad?'

Going Private

'We're not laying cables,
we're burying some of
our money'

Soviet Disunion
Post-Gorbachev, the Army and KGB were reformed

'Another coup against Mr Gorbachev hardly seems worth the trouble now'

'There goes another supporter of the coup'

Soviet Disunion

There was competition for the Russian presidency

'In years to come we'll remember exactly what we were queuing for when we heard the news'

'Just a minute . . .'

Soviet Disunion

There were weapons everywhere

'*Right, Estonia has them on Mondays and Thursdays, Moldavia has them . . .*'

'*How quickly can you change a gulf war sandpit into a map of the USSR?*'

Soviet Disunion

Cold War hardware was dismantled

*'This always happens
when you leave an empty
skip outside'*

Soviet Disunion
As prices soared, the West promised aid

'Do you have any potatoes
that are slightly more
communist?'

'They're not what I was
expecting, but it's very
kind of Mr Major'

Doctor's Orders

Doctors now control their own budgets . . .

'I hear you now control your own budget, doctor'

'I pulled a muscle in the standing ovation after the health debate'

Doctor's Orders

... Dentists have had theirs cut

'Would you like to spit?'

'Instead of a health debate
we'll all take two aspirins
and come back in the morning'

Farewell, then, Captain Bob

The Maxwell brothers declined to answer
MP's questions

'You let the Maxwells
go home?'

'Darling, you would tell me
if you owed someone £½bn,
wouldn't you?'